Draw a circle around the world with your finger.

God made the bright blue sky.

6

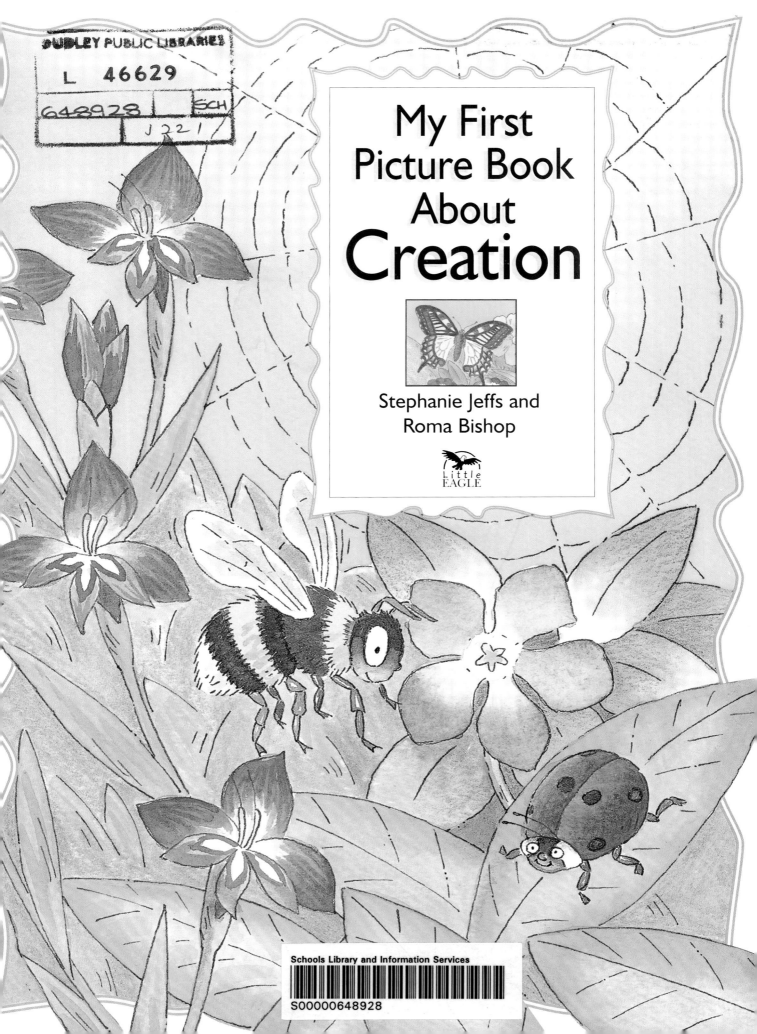

My First
Picture Book
About
Creation

Stephanie Jeffs and
Roma Bishop

Little
EAGLE

God made our big, round world.

Find the fluffy cloud floating in the sky.

God made the splishy splashy sea.

8

Can you find the waves rolling through the sea?

God made the big tall mountains.

Point to the tops of the mountains.

Can you see the juicy strawberries?

God made the bright golden sun.

Touch the sun!

Can you find four stars
shining in the sky?

God made the flippy flappy fishes.

Can you find the starfish
at the bottom of the sea?

Can you see the baby ducks
swimming on the pond?

God made the skidding scuttling spider.

Where is the ladybird
and the busy buzzing bee?

24

Can you see a zebra
and an elephant too?

27

Can you find the baby goats playing near their mother?

Published in the UK by Eagle Publishing
PO Box 530, Guildford, Surrey GU2 4FH
ISBN 0 86347 409 8

First edition 2001

Copyright © 2001 AD Publishing Services Ltd
1 Churchgates, The Wilderness, Berkhamsted, Herts HP4 2UB
Illustrations copyright © 2001 Roma Bishop

British Library Cataloguing in Publication Data.
A catalogue record for this book is available from the British Library.

Printed in Hong Kong